5 Flowers, 4 Stories, 3 Cheers for ANIMALS!

Chair,
National Board
of Directors

Chief
Executive
Officer

Chief
Operating
Officer

Vice
President,
Program

Connie L. Lindsey

Anna Maria Chávez

Jan Verhage

Eileen Doyle

PHOTOGRAPHS
Pages 15 and 22: Sharon Beals; **Page 38:** Art
© Deborah Butterfield/Licensed by VAGA,
New York, NY; **Page 49:** © 2010 Artists
Rights Society (ARS), New York/ADAPG,
Paris; Digital Image © 2009 Museum
Associates/LACMA/Art Resource, NY; **Page
52:** Robert Anyon; **Page 73:** Justin Sutcliffe

This publication was made possible by a generous
grant from the Dove Self-Esteem Fund.

SENIOR DIRECTOR, PROGRAM RESOURCES: Suzanne Harper

ART DIRECTOR: Douglas Bantz

WRITERS: Alice Carpenter, Valerie Takahama, Carol Fleishman,
Laura J. Tuchman, Andrea Bastiani Archibald

ILLUSTRATOR: Susan Swan

DESIGNER: Sara Gillingham for Charette Communication Design

PROGRAM TEAM: Ellen Kelliher, Sarah Micklem,
Sheryl O'Connell, Lesley Williams

© 2010 by Girl Scouts of the USA

First published in 2010 by Girl Scouts of the USA
420 Fifth Avenue, New York, NY 10018-2798

www.girlscouts.org

ISBN: 978-0-88441-749-1

Printed in Italy

5 6 7 8 9/18 17 16 15 14

Text printed on Fedrigoni Cento 40
percent de-inked, post-consumer fibers
and 60 percent secondary recycled
fibers. Covers printed on Prisma artboard
FSC® Certified mixed sources.

MIX
Paper from
responsible sources
FSC® C115118

FSC
www.fsc.org

What's Inside?

Welcome to This Amazing Animal Adventure

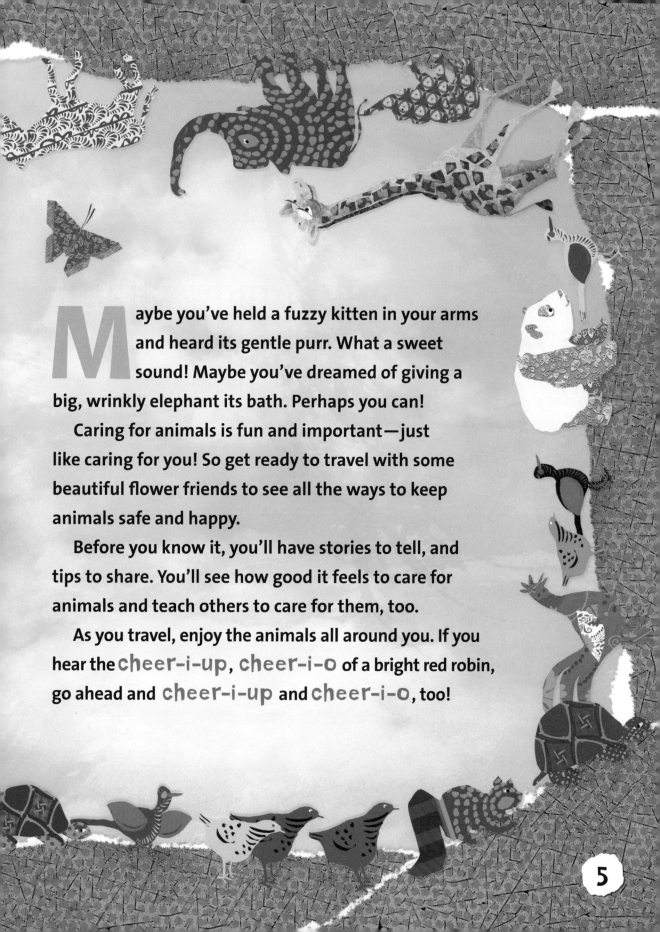

Maybe you've held a fuzzy kitten in your arms and heard its gentle purr. What a sweet sound! Maybe you've dreamed of giving a big, wrinkly elephant its bath. Perhaps you can!

Caring for animals is fun and important—just like caring for you! So get ready to travel with some beautiful flower friends to see all the ways to keep animals safe and happy.

Before you know it, you'll have stories to tell, and tips to share. You'll see how good it feels to care for animals and teach others to care for them, too.

As you travel, enjoy the animals all around you. If you hear the cheer-i-up, cheer-i-o of a bright red robin, go ahead and cheer-i-up and cheer-i-o, too!

A Purr-fect Surprise in the Garden

It was a beautiful morning in the Daisy Flower Garden. A soft breeze blew through the trees. Honeybees hummed. Butterflies danced from flower to flower. Tiny birds sang early-morning songs in their cozy nests.

Tula, the tulip, stretched her red petals toward the golden sun. "Our garden is home to so many critters," she said. "It's so nice that we share our garden with so many living things."

Come Out, Come Out . . . Wherever You Are!

Lots of critters live in the Daisy Flower Garden. How many can you find?

"Yes," agreed Mari, the marigold. "Birds, squirrels, and chipmunks are busy in the trees. And wiggling worms live in our soil. From top to bottom, our garden is a wonderful place!"

Vi, the violet, started to giggle.

"What is it, Vi?" Tula asked.

"That butterfly tickled me when she stopped to sip my nectar," Vi said. "Taking care of our garden critters is so much fun!"

Just then, the flower friends heard a strange sound. "MEOW-W-W-W!"

"What could that be?" asked Vi.

Was it a chipmunk? No! A squirrel? No!

"Look!" said Tula. "It's a sweet little cat."

Vi peeked at the cat. It *was* little. But Vi wasn't so sure it was sweet. It was loud!

"I like to be very careful when there's a new critter around," Vi said.

Tula looked closer at the cat. "I think she's trying to tell us something. Maybe she's thirsty."

"I've seen many cats on my travels," said Mari.

"Big or small, they all need the same things we do to stay healthy and safe. Let's get this cat a sip of water from our pond."

"That's a great idea," said Tula. "We can have a sip, too. We don't want to get droopy!"

Just then, Robin, the red robin, flew by. "Cats need exercise, too," she chirped. "I can help with that." She flew this way and that.

Sing Out and Smile!

Robins can sing when breathing in or breathing out. So they can sing long, cheerful songs without stopping. How long can you sing without stopping?

The cat followed, running and jumping playfully. Soon a dazzling butterfly caught the cat's eye . . . jump, jump, bump! The cat ran after the butterfly. All around the garden they went.

The butterfly flew. The cat jumped and bumped!

The cat was so busy playing, she didn't notice the butterfly was headed straight for the pond! Would this cat know how to swim? Tula raced to the pond. She stopped just in front of the cat.

"Stay," Tula said in a firm but gentle voice. The cat rubbed against Tula, with a grateful purr. Tula smiled.

"Tula," said Vi, "you reached the pond just in time. That was fast thinking."

"And brave thinking, too," said Mari.

The cat purred again. It stretched and yawned. Then it curled up on the grass.

"This cat looks sleepy," said Tula. "Maybe she'd like to take a **catnap**."

Tula spread her petals to make a shady spot for the cat to rest in. The cat purred as the flowers took turns petting her.

WORDS FOR THE WISE

A **CATNAP** is a short nap. A catnap can make you feel rested and refreshed.

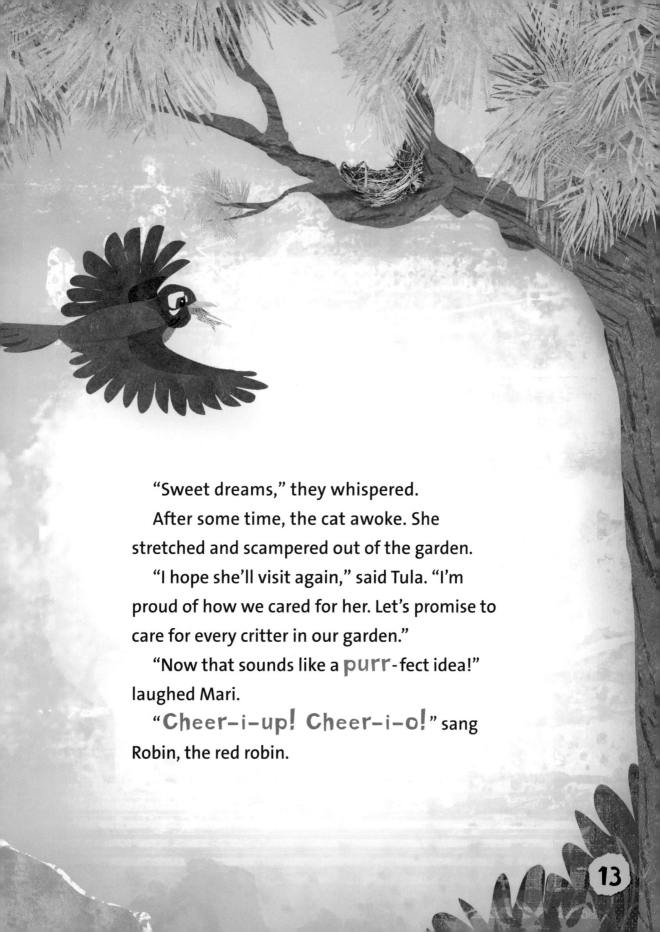

"Sweet dreams," they whispered.

After some time, the cat awoke. She stretched and scampered out of the garden.

"I hope she'll visit again," said Tula. "I'm proud of how we cared for her. Let's promise to care for every critter in our garden."

"Now that sounds like a purr-fect idea!" laughed Mari.

"Cheer-i-up! Cheer-i-o!" sang Robin, the red robin.

WHEN A CAMERA MEETS A NEST

Did you ever wish you could peek inside a bird's nest? **Sharon Beals's** photographs let you do just that. She photographs nests collected by scientists and stored for safekeeping in museums. Some of them are 100 years old!

Sharon's photographs let you see what nests are made of. Sometimes birds build nests with whatever they can find, like bits of paper, string, and ribbon. Birds can even make nests from nails. Ouch! Nails don't sound cozy!

"I hope that my art makes people curious about birds' nests," Sharon says. "As we learn more about nests, we learn how to keep birds' homes safe and protected."

One way to care for birds, says Sharon, is to plant bushes and flowers that they can enjoy.

Big Nests, Little Nests

A bald eagle's nest can be very big. It can weigh as much as a hippopotamus! The nest of a hummingbird can be so small, a coin can cover it. Who are the best nest-builders? Small birds! Why? Their little beaks can weave nests from string and ribbon, and other itty-bitty things.

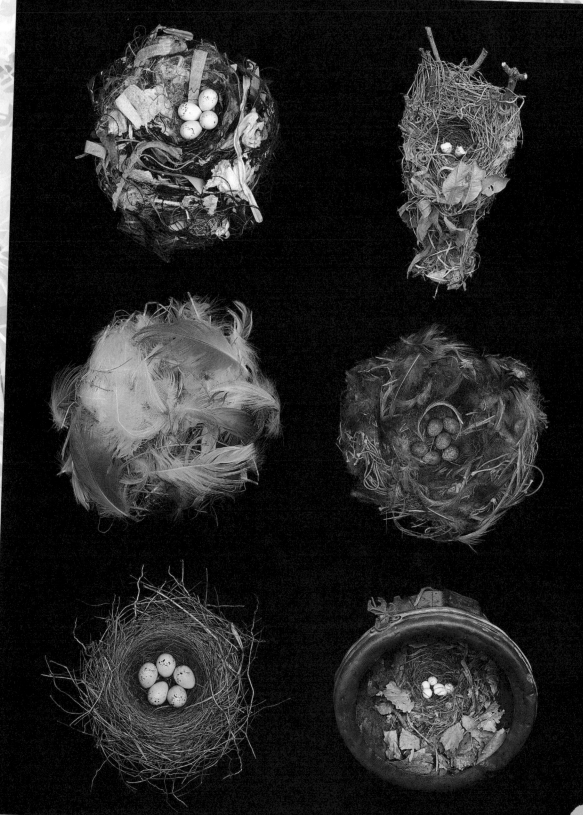

WORDS FOR THE WISE

To **INCH** means to move just a bit at a time. An inch can also mean a small length of something. An inch of string is something a small bird might add to its nest.

THE FIRST STORIES
A Little Birdie Told Me . . .

Splash! Robin, the red robin, splashed and splashed in the garden's birdbath. She was as happy as could be.

"I wonder how Robin became so red," said Gloria, the morning glory.

"I wonder how *I* came to be red," Tula said.

"Maybe there are stories for how we got our colors," said Mari as she looked at her own petals, which were the color of a ripe orange.

"Let's make up our own stories!" said Tula.

"I'll start!" said Zinni, the zinnia. "One day a tiny caterpillar inched along through the spring-green grass. Soon that caterpillar was spring-green, too. Then the caterpillar inched along my petals. Before long, my petals turned a bright, spring-green, too!"

"In time, the caterpillar became a beautiful, orange butterfly," Mari said. "The butterfly rubbed her silky wings against me as she stopped to rest. And just like that, I became as orange as the butterfly!"

"And then a spring shower came," said Vi.

"We love spring showers!" the flower friends all shouted.

"It rained
and rained," Vi said
with a smile. "But when
the sun began to shine, a
rainbow stretched across the
sky. The colors mixed together
into a beautiful shade of purple
known as violet. The color came drip-
dropping down on my petals. And
that's why I am the color violet."

"Soon evening came and the sky filled with stars," said Gloria, the morning glory. "The dark starry sky fell upon my petals, covering me in a deep shade of purple. That's why I am deep purple."

"What a wonderful story," said Tula.

"Now it's your turn, Tula," said Zinni.

Tula sat quietly for a moment, just thinking.

The flower friends waited patiently.

Finally, Tula said: "When morning came, a red robin awoke and stretched. A single, red feather came tumbling from her nest. I reached up and caught that red feather. Then I used it to paint all my petals red."

The flower friends applauded.

"We did it," said Tula. "We told a great story. And each part of the story is as special as we are."

"Cheer-i-up! Cheer-i-o!" sang Robin, the red robin. "What about me?" she asked. "Is there time for one more story?"

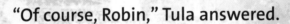

"Of course, Robin," Tula answered.

Robin began: "Once, there was a red robin. This robin had an orange-red breast. She had cousins who were brown and gray."

"Oh, that's just like my family!" shouted Gloria. "We are alike in many ways, but we are many colors." Gloria blushed a little. "I interrupted your story! Please, go on."

A Nest Worth Sleeping In!

Look at this nest, built inside a shiny bowl! If you could build a nest anywhere, where would you build it?

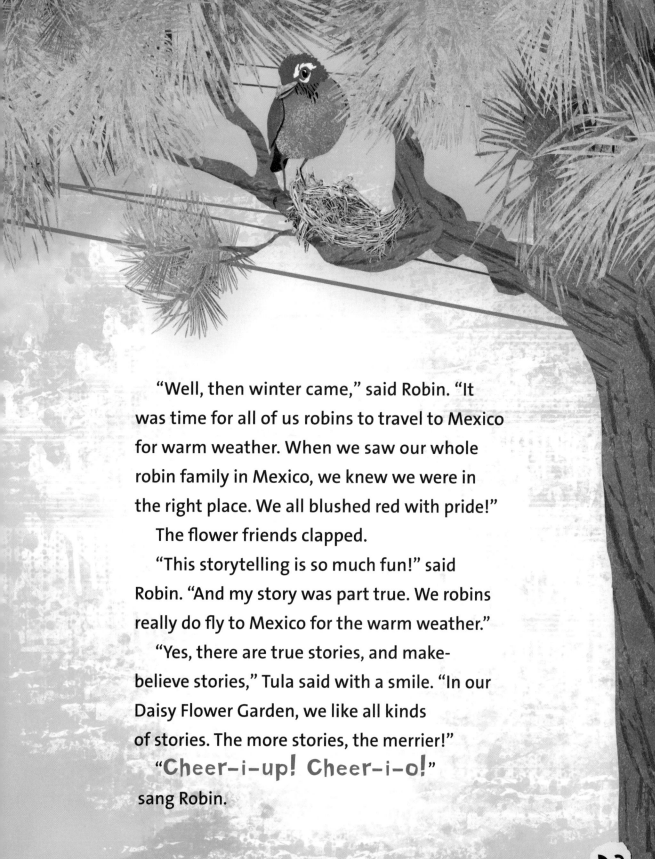

"Well, then winter came," said Robin. "It was time for all of us robins to travel to Mexico for warm weather. When we saw our whole robin family in Mexico, we knew we were in the right place. We all blushed red with pride!"

The flower friends clapped.

"This storytelling is so much fun!" said Robin. "And my story was part true. We robins really do fly to Mexico for the warm weather."

"Yes, there are true stories, and make-believe stories," Tula said with a smile. "In our Daisy Flower Garden, we like all kinds of stories. The more stories, the merrier!"

"Cheer-i-up! Cheer-i-o!" sang Robin.

TELL YOUR STORY!

Make It True . . .

I became a Girl Scout Daisy when I was _____.

My Daisy group meets at _____.

My favorite things to do as a Daisy are _____

and _____.

Now, Make It Pretend!

One day, my friend and I took a walk to the park.

On the way, we met a big, polka-dotted hippo.

Finish this story any way you want, in pictures or words!

If I were a bird

If I were a bird, my feathers would be the color _____.

I would fly to _____.

I would look like this:

Not all robins are red

Many robins' breasts are orange-red breasts. Others are pale gray or brown.

Not Just for Birds!

Mice, turtles, and alligators build nests, too.

LEARNING ABOUT SEA TURTLES

Melissa Ocana

loves to learn about animals. When she was young, she read about animals and watched animals. She even watched squirrels chasing one another in her backyard.

Now Melissa watches sea turtles. She has traveled to Mexico and other countries to learn more about them. Sea turtles live in the ocean, but they build their nests on land.

Melissa knows that caring for sea turtles means making sure that they have safe, clean places to build their nests. And she knows that can begin in her own backyard. "It's important to keep the oceans, seas, and our land litter free," Melissa says.

How can you make things safe for animals where you live? How can you make where you live safe for you?

Cousin Sara

Aunt Sofia

MARKET

Aunt Teresa   Uncle Jobim

ZINNI'S STORY
¡Bienvenido a Mèxico!

Welcome to Mexico! Zinni, the zinnia, opened her photo album. It was filled with pictures of her visit with her family in Mexico. The flower friends loved seeing pictures of Zinni's colorful cousins. They were lavender, pink, purple, rose, and even yellow.

"All beautiful *colores*," Zinni said proudly. "*Colores* is the Spanish word for colors."

Zinni turned the page. The flower friends squealed with delight. A tall, brown horse gazed out with gentle eyes. The horse reminded Zinni of an adventure at her cousins' farm in Mexico.

MY ENERGY SNACKS

Horses eat apples and oats. These snacks give them energy to gallop!
What snacks give you energy?

_____

_____

_____

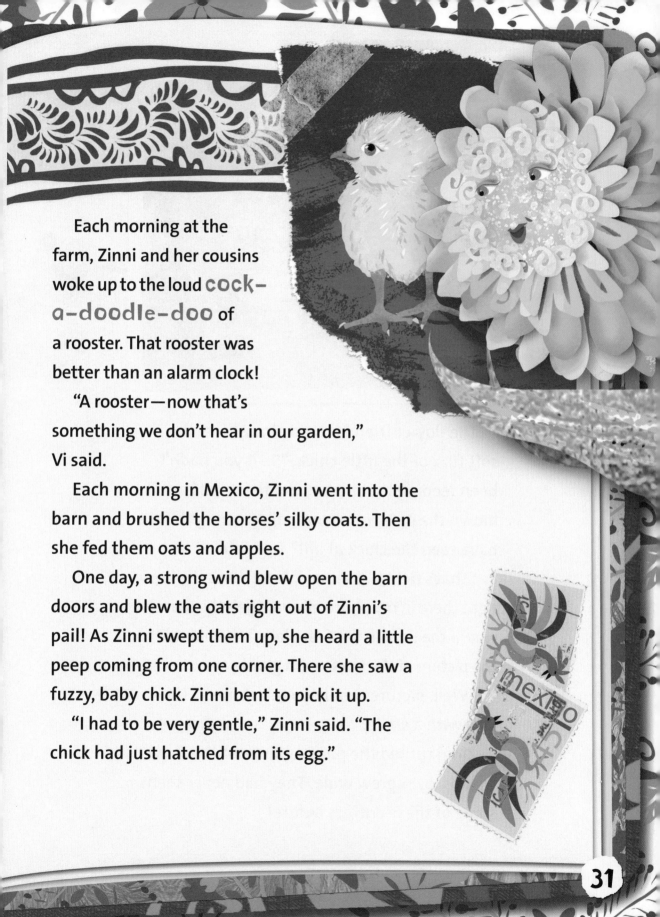

Each morning at the farm, Zinni and her cousins woke up to the loud cock-a-doodle-doo of a rooster. That rooster was better than an alarm clock!

"A rooster—now that's something we don't hear in our garden," Vi said.

Each morning in Mexico, Zinni went into the barn and brushed the horses' silky coats. Then she fed them oats and apples.

One day, a strong wind blew open the barn doors and blew the oats right out of Zinni's pail! As Zinni swept them up, she heard a little peep coming from one corner. There she saw a fuzzy, baby chick. Zinni bent to pick it up.

"I had to be very gentle," Zinni said. "The chick had just hatched from its egg."

The flower friends could almost feel the soft fuzz of the little chick. "So if you hadn't been feeding that horse, and the wind hadn't blown the oats from your pail, you might not have seen the chick at all!" Tula said.

"That's right," Zinni said, "and that's the horse, right there in my photo album. She's the reason I was in the barn in the first place." She pointed to the picture of the horse with gentle eyes.

"Well, pictures really do tell stories," Tula said with a smile.

Zinni turned the page again, and the flower friends' eyes grew wide. They had never seen some of these critters before!

"What is that animal that looks like a little horse?" Vi asked. "It's cute!"

Zinni explained that it was a burro. The burro carried hay to the barn in a wagon. It also carried the tasty fruits and vegetables that were grown on the farm.

"We ate lots of those vegetables with my aunt's delicious quesadillas," said Zinni. "We ate peppers, avocados, and beans, too. Those foods are really good—and good for you."

WORDS FOR THE WISE

QUESADILLAS

(pronounced: case-a-DEE-yas) are tortillas filled with melted cheese. *Queso* is the Spanish word for cheese! They're easy to make. Ask an adult to help you. You might even put a few vegetables inside!

"I guess you could say the burro helped everyone stay healthy," said Mari.

Zinni closed her photo album. "There's just one problem," she said.

"What's that?" asked Vi.

"These pictures remind me of all the fun I had in Mexico. But they also remind me that I really miss my family," said Zinni.

"I have an idea," said Gloria. "My family just sent me a postcard from Japan. Postcards are a nice way to keep in touch. Why don't you mail a postcard to your family in Mexico? Then maybe they'll send a postcard back to you!"

"That's a good idea," said Zinni. "I love getting mail; I bet they do, too. Let's all get together and take our picture for the postcard."

"Cheer-i-up! Cheer-i-o!" sang Robin, the red robin. "I'll take the picture for you, Zinni. Now, smile, everyone! And say 'Cheese!'"

"No, say 'QUESO!'" Mari shouted. And then all the flowers laughed.

Donkeys, Horses, Zebras! Oh, My!

Horses look a bit like donkeys. Horses also look a bit like zebras. Finish this picture any way you like. Will you make an animal that is part zebra and part something else? The choice is up to you!

TELL YOUR STORY!

When I was small, _____took care of me.

I couldn't _____.

Now that I'm older, I can _____.

This makes me feel _____.

Draw a picture that shows you taking care of yourself.

A LOVE OF HORSES

Deborah Butterfield loves horses. She shares her love of horses by making sculptures of them.

Some of Deborah's horse sculptures are bigger than real horses! She makes them from things she finds lying around, like metal that people throw away, or wood on the beach.

Some of Deborah's horses stand quietly. Others look like they are resting. Some even look like they are eating.

Deborah hopes her horses will make you think about ways to care for animals. Animals, she says, "can teach us to be quiet, to listen and watch to understand the needs of others. . . . They can show us how to be happy for the smallest things."

Exercises to Try with Friends

Galloping like a horse is fun, of course. There are many other ways to get exercise. Which would you like to try?

- ❑ Jump rope
- ❑ Jumping jacks
- ❑ Toss and catch a ball
- ❑ Bouncing a ball against a wall
- ❑ Skip and hop
- ❑ Hopscotch
- ❑ Dance

Imagine making an animal out of things and stuff! Get together with friends and see what you can find. Then make a favorite animal!

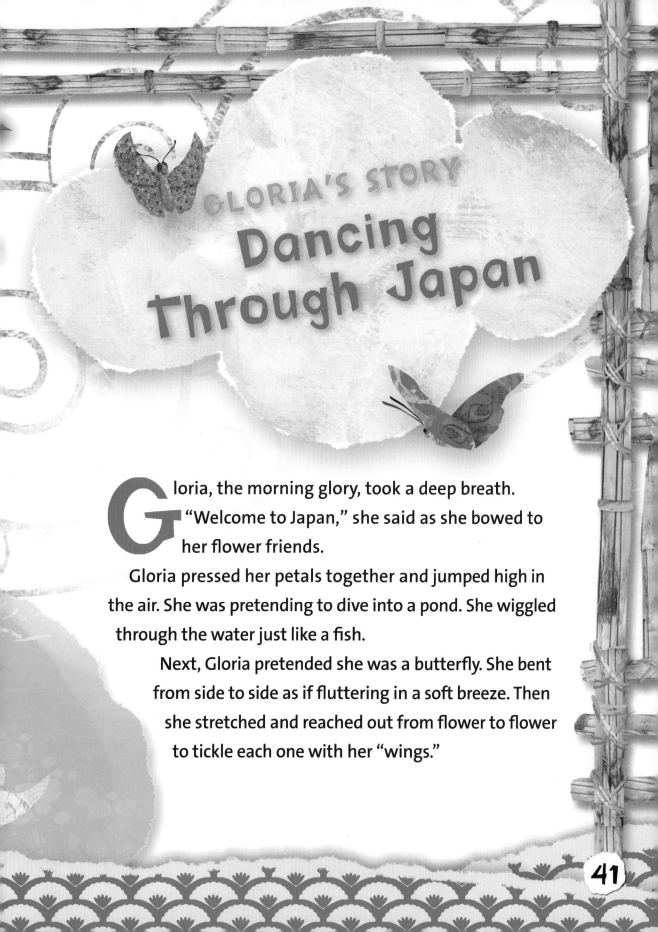

GLORIA'S STORY
Dancing Through Japan

Gloria, the morning glory, took a deep breath. "Welcome to Japan," she said as she bowed to her flower friends.

Gloria pressed her petals together and jumped high in the air. She was pretending to dive into a pond. She wiggled through the water just like a fish.

Next, Gloria pretended she was a butterfly. She bent from side to side as if fluttering in a soft breeze. Then she stretched and reached out from flower to flower to tickle each one with her "wings."

Tula laughed.

Gloria smiled but didn't say a word. She now pretended to be a turtle. She curled up on the ground and made herself as small as she could be. Inch by inch, she poked out her face and peeked up at her friends.

"You look just like a turtle!" said Mari. "I think you are showing us the animals you saw when you traveled to Japan!"

"That's right," said Gloria. Then she bowed again. Next, she stretched up high and held her petals still. She was pretending to be a big, graceful bird called a Japanese crane.

Gloria bowed once more. It was time to pretend to be one last animal. She spread her petals wide. She skipped and rolled and bounced along happily. Next, she sat on the ground and munched and munched. Then she munched some more.

At last, Gloria yawned and stretched. She even rubbed her belly! Then she settled down for a nap.

But Gloria wasn't finished!

Suddenly she jumped up and pretended she was carrying something very special. She handed that special something to her friends with a deep bow.

What could it be? The flower friends thought and thought. But none could guess what Gloria was showing them.

"It's not an animal we ever see in our garden," Gloria said. "But it's my favorite animal in the whole world! It's a Giant Panda."

"I thought you were carrying a gift," Vi said.

"The Giant Panda *was* a gift," said Gloria. "It was a gift from the people of China to the people of Japan."

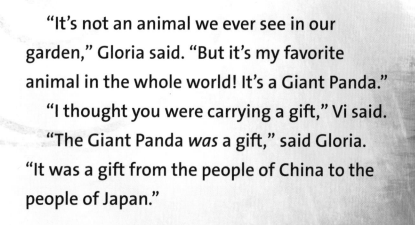

Pandas and Me!

Eating bamboo keeps pandas healthy. It keeps pandas' teeth strong, too.

I need _____ and _____

to keep my teeth strong and healthy.

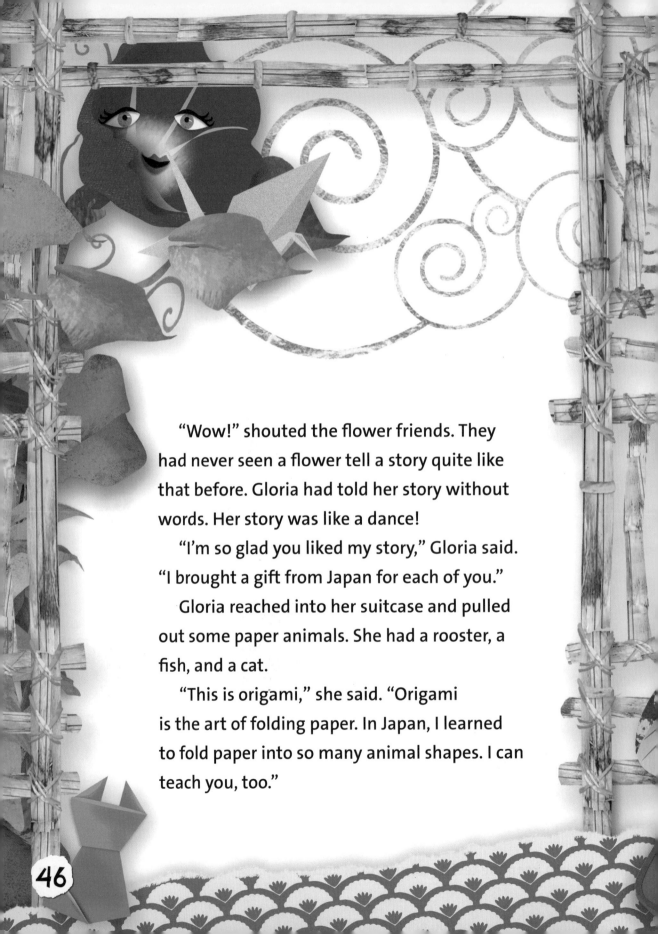

"Wow!" shouted the flower friends. They had never seen a flower tell a story quite like that before. Gloria had told her story without words. Her story was like a dance!

"I'm so glad you liked my story," Gloria said. "I brought a gift from Japan for each of you."

Gloria reached into her suitcase and pulled out some paper animals. She had a rooster, a fish, and a cat.

"This is origami," she said. "Origami is the art of folding paper. In Japan, I learned to fold paper into so many animal shapes. I can teach you, too."

Soon the flower friends were busy making their own origami animals. In no time at all, the Daisy Flower Garden was filled with animals in all colors of the rainbow!

Gloria's Suitcase

How many things from Japan can you name in Gloria's suitcase?

47

Tell a Story Without Words!

Animals can tell you how they feel without using words. A dog wags its tail to tell you it is happy. An animal with its ears pointed back may be frightened.

Can you tell how these flower friends are feeling? Match the flowers to what they are feeling. Then decide what you would want to say to them.

Mad	Sad	Happy
_____	_____	_____
_____	_____	_____
_____	_____	_____

A BIRD IN SPACE

Constantin Brancusi was an artist who worked in Paris, a city in France that is famous for art. Constantin liked to make sculptures in the shapes of birds.

In his sculptures, you might not see the bird's head or wings or tail. But you can feel the bird soaring!

Imagine that you are one of Constantin's birds. Stretch your wings! Soar and glide!

Do you think Constantin's art tells the story of a gentle bird? A happy bird? A busy bird? A quiet bird? A courageous bird?

Japanese Garden Yoga

Try these fun ways to move like animals!
Start with a deep breath in, and finish
with a deep breath out. Put on some
soft, quiet music for extra fun.

THE BUTTERFLY

Sitting down, press the bottoms of your feet
together. Keep your back straight.
Now, gently rock your knees
up and down, just like
butterfly wings!

THE TURTLE

Curl up on the floor. Tuck your knees under your tummy. Round your back as if you were a turtle in its shell. Slowly stretch one arm forward, then slowly bring it back. Repeat with one arm at a time, then one leg at a time. Stretch your neck, too.

THE CRANE

Stand on both feet, keeping both knees facing straight ahead. Lift one leg, touching your foot to your knee. To balance, put your arms out just like wings. This may take some practice!

TURNING PAPER INTO ART

In Japan, folding squares of paper into shapes like flowers, birds, cats, horses, and roosters is an art. It's called origami. **Florence Temko** was an expert in the art of origami. She thought up new origami shapes and she traveled far and wide to share her love of origami. Some of her favorite origami shapes were holiday decorations, kites, stars, and candles. Florence wrote books about origami. She showed her creations on television, too. All over the world, Florence made friends through her love of origami. She taught origami to many Girl Scouts, and those Girl Scouts shared their origami with girls all around the world.

Here's a fun origami shape for you to try. Just follow the directions, step by step!

Cat

First, make the HEAD.

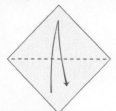
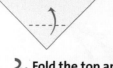
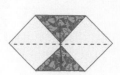

1. Hold a square of paper with one corner up. Fold the square in half so the top corner covers the bottom corner. Then unfold the square.

2. Fold the top and bottom corners to meet the center fold.

3. Fold in half.

4. Flip it over, so the long, flat side is up.

5. Fold up the sides to make the cat's ears.

6. Flip it over! You have your cat's head!

Now, make the BODY.

1. Fold another square in half, just like you did for the head. But this time, keep the square folded with a flat side down.

2. Fold up the right bottom corner to make a tail.

3. Now you have the cat's body!

Your cat comes together when you put the top corner of the body into the pocket of the head (near the cat's chin).

Your Cat Can Stand Up!

Just unfold the tail a little bit.

Make a Whole Cat Family!

Use smaller squares of paper for the kittens, and bigger squares for the mom and dad.

MARI'S STORY
Rumbles and Roars

A cool rain fell on the Daisy Flower Garden. The flower friends giggled as rain danced on their petals.

"This is almost as much fun as an elephant's shower," Mari, the marigold, said with a laugh. "An elephant's shower is the biggest shower I've ever seen!"

Soon Mari was telling about her trip to Africa. There, she watched elephants bathe their babies. First, the baby elephants held tight to their mother's tails. Then they marched in a big line to the watering hole. What a parade!

Soon the mothers were slurping up water with their long trunks. When their trunks were full . . . splash! They sprayed cool water all over their babies. Over and over, the big elephants sprayed the babies. They sprayed until the babies were squeaky clean.

WORDS FOR THE WISE

TRUNKS!

There are many kinds of TRUNKS! The strong, bark-covered base of a tree is a trunk. The trunk of a car is like a closet. Some big suitcases are called trunks. The most amazing trunk of all may be the elephant's long nose.

"Then the babies began to squirt each other," said Mari.

"They were playing!" Vi shouted. "They can play and get clean at the same time, just like us. Playing and keeping clean always makes me feel really good!"

Mari remembered one baby elephant who was the smallest of all. When this little elephant tried to spray water from her trunk, nothing came out! The little elephant dipped her trunk into the water again and again. Finally, only a tiny trickle of water spilled out.

"Did she give up?" asked Tula.

"No," said Mari. "She kept trying!"

Soon the mother elephants lifted their trunks into the air. They made a loud sound, just like a trumpet! Bath time was over! The babies climbed out of the water. Each one found its mother's tail. All except that one small elephant. Her mother called again for the baby to come out of the water.

And just then, a big spray of water splashed over all the mother elephants and the little elephants, too. When they looked around, they saw the smallest elephant shake the last drops of water from her trunk. Then she marched proudly out of the watering hole. She had finally learned to spray!

"Her spray even hit my petals!" Mari said.

As the elephants marched home, they lifted their trunks high and trumpeted loudly. The little elephant lifted her trunk, too. She made a soft "Toot, toot" sound. "That really made me smile," Mari said.

Elephants and Me!

Elephants use their trunk to smell. I use my _____.

Elephants use their trunk to wash. I use my _____.

Elephants can run, climb, and swim. But elephants cannot jump.

What do you do well? _____.

Mari told the flower friends how she saw other big animals in Africa, too. She saw a giraffe stretch its long neck to reach high into the trees to munch on leaves. "Just then, two big parrots flew out of the trees and I heard a mighty roar," Mari said.

"Was it a lion?" asked Vi.

"No," said Mari. "It was one of the parrots! She was roaring, just like the lions. Parrots copy what they hear. And guess what? She had a bright red tail, brighter than our friend Robin."

"Did someone say red? Cheer–i–up! Cheer–i–o!" sang Robin. She was busy on the ground, collecting twigs and leaves.

"I'm making my nest cozy," she said. "We'll soon have baby robins in our flower garden."

"What exciting news!" said Tula. "Maybe we can help build your nest!" And with that, the flower friends began to search for twigs and leaves, too.

Big Cat Facts

Cheetahs belong to the same family as house cats, but they can move as fast as a fast-moving car!

Daisy and Her Animal Friends

Juliette "Daisy" Gordon Low started Girl Scouts. Daisy loved animals of every kind. "An animal can be a best friend in life," she said. One of her favorite pets was a parrot named Polly Poons.

What would you name a parrot?

_____

ANIMALS ARE LIKE PEOPLE

Just after **Irene Pepperberg** turned 4, she was given a baby parakeet. She started talking to the parakeet right away.

When Irene grew up, she began to study how parrots think, talk, and learn. She studied an African Grey parrot named Alex. Alex became her dear friend.

Alex learned to speak and count, and he learned shapes and colors. If Alex misbehaved, he would say, "I'm sorry." When he was hungry, he would say, "Wanna nut" or "Wanna banana."

Alex taught Irene how much animals are like people. Irene wrote a book in which she shares many stories, so that others can learn how much animals are like people too.

"Through my work with Alex, I learned to have patience," Irene says. "I also learned to look at humans as a part of nature."

Home, Sweet Home

The flower friends spread out through the garden. They gathered soft moss and crunchy leaves for Robin's nest. It felt good to share all that the garden offered.

"I'm a very fast worker when it comes to building my nest," Robin said. "But this is the kindest thing anyone has ever done for me. Thank you for your help, flower friends. Cheer-i-up! Cheer-i-o!"

"We can hardly wait for your baby robins to become part of our garden family. Maybe we can find worms for them to eat," Zinni said.

"Until then, we have lots of other garden friends to help," said Tula. "We've learned how important it is to care for other living creatures. Now, let's be sure to take good care of ourselves. That way, we'll be ready to care for others. Let's promise to keep our Daisy Flower Garden strong and healthy for all its critters."

"Let's promise to make sure there are plenty of leaves and branches, for the birds and squirrels to build nests with," said Vi.

"And lots of crunchy seeds for them to eat," said Zinni.

"Let's promise to keep fresh water in our birdbath and pond. Then our critters can drink, bathe, and enjoy splashing about," said Gloria.

"Let's promise to do our part to care for animals here at home and far, far away, too. We've learned so much from everyone's stories," said Mari. "It's important that we share our stories. The more we teach others, the more others can care for animals, too."

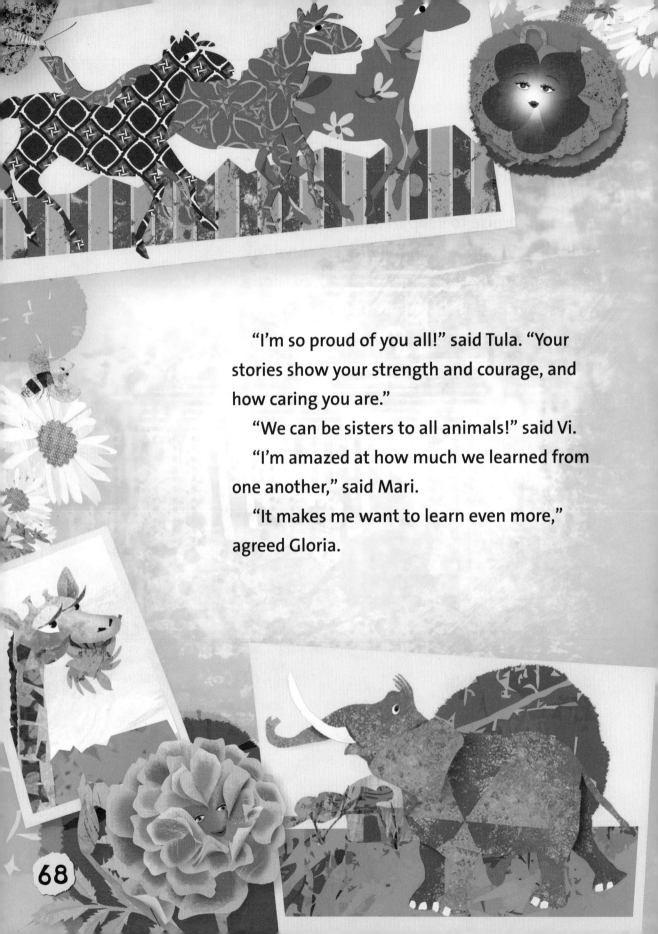

"I'm so proud of you all!" said Tula. "Your stories show your strength and courage, and how caring you are."

"We can be sisters to all animals!" said Vi.

"I'm amazed at how much we learned from one another," said Mari.

"It makes me want to learn even more," agreed Gloria.

"I never expected to feel so proud of what I can do. It was one of the best surprises ever," said Zinni.

"I felt really important to care for animals," said Vi, "even if I was a little nervous at first."

"We all have lots of feelings inside us," said Tula. "It feels good to share our feelings.

69

"It's important that we try to understand how others feel, too. I'm proud that you trusted us enough to share your feelings."

Vi smiled. She looked around the Daisy Flower Garden. Birds chirped. Bees buzzed. Chipmunks chattered. Just then, the flower friends heard a familiar sound.

"MEOW– W– W– W!"

"It's the cat," said Vi. "She's back!"

"And she brought her kittens," said Gloria.

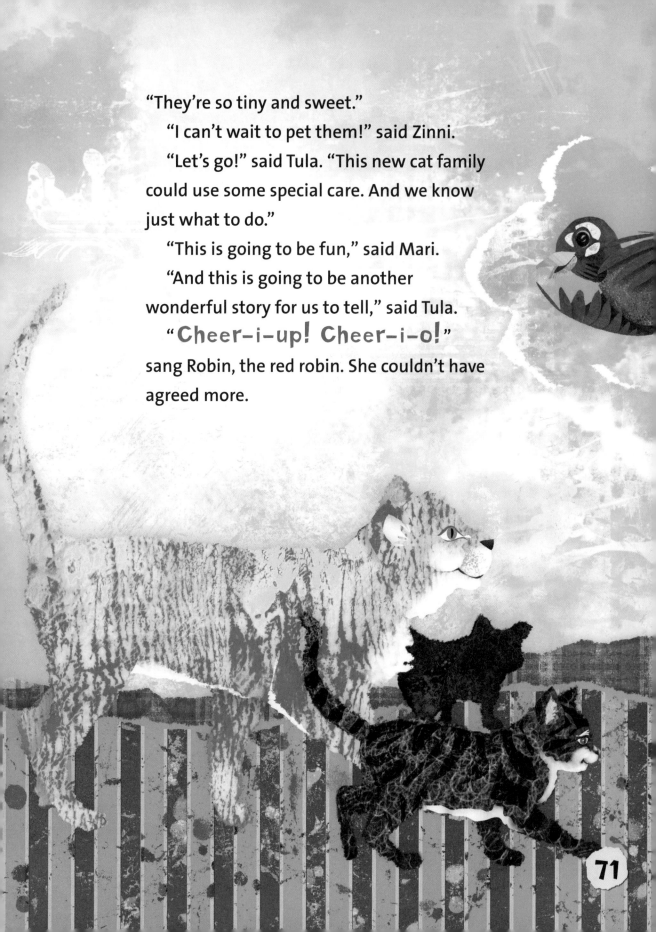

"They're so tiny and sweet."

"I can't wait to pet them!" said Zinni.

"Let's go!" said Tula. "This new cat family could use some special care. And we know just what to do."

"This is going to be fun," said Mari.

"And this is going to be another wonderful story for us to tell," said Tula.

"Cheer-i-up! Cheer-i-o!" sang Robin, the red robin. She couldn't have agreed more.

PEOPLE CAN CARE FOR ANIMALS

Nia Perkins had hamsters, rabbits, and birds as pets when she was growing up. When she was 12, her hamster, Slade, got sick. A doctor for animals helped Slade get better. "I knew from that point what I was going to do," Nia says.

That summer, she volunteered at the office of the veterinarian who helped her hamster. She watched the vet examine pets. She even watched the vet perform operations.

Nia studied biology and chemistry in high school and college. That's how she became the vet she is today!

Nia now takes care of animals in Alexandria, Virginia. "I check them out from head to toe," she says.

ANIMALS CAN CARE FOR PEOPLE, TOO!

Stephanie Calmenson knows that animals can care for people. Her dog, Rosie, visits people to make them happy. Some of them are children and older people who are sad or sick or lonely. They all feel better after seeing Rosie. Sometimes they even brush Rosie's fur.

Rosie knows her work is important. She wears a special badge and leash. And she holds her head high to show how proud she is.

When Rosie visits people, she likes to roll over and have her belly rubbed. And that makes the people Rosie visits laugh and feel happy too.

ANIMAL Snacks

Snacks can be fun to make, fun to look at, and fun to eat. Which of these snacks would you like? Try one with your family!

Apple Ladybugs

1. Ask an adult to core an apple for you and slice it in half from top to bottom.

2. Place the halves, flat side down, on a small plate.

3. Dab some yogurt cheese or peanut butter, or a topping of your choice, on the skin side of the apple halves.

4. Stick raisins on the dabs to make the ladybug's spots and eyes.

5. Make antennae by putting one end of a pretzel stick into a raisin, then pressing the other end into the apple.

6. Now you have two ladybugs. Enjoy one and give the other to a friend!

Incredible, Edible Nests

You can build a nest that's yummy enough to eat!
Here's what you'll need:

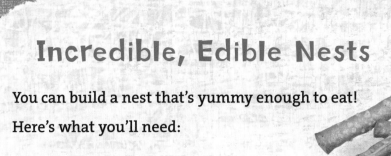

Pretzel sticks
1/2 cup shredded carrots
1/2 cup peanut butter or yogurt cheese

Mix together carrots and peanut butter or yogurt cheese. Shape the mixture into a hollow cup. Cover your mixture with pretzel sticks. They'll look like twigs! Then enjoy your snack. Chew carefully!

Ants on a Log

Spread yogurt cheese, hummus, or peanut butter inside the hollow of a celery stalk. Use raisins as "ants" to decorate the "logs." Then enjoy!

HOW DOGS HELP PEOPLE SEE

When **Karlie Jackson** was 12, she started raising a puppy named Olympia. Olympia was a yellow Labrador retriever. She was going to be a guide dog for people who can't see well.

Karlie took Olympia to training classes, and to school, soccer games, and church. That way, Olympia got used to new sights and sounds, and lots of people.

Karlie taught her classmates that guide dogs can change the life of someone who can't see well.

Karlie is now raising a second puppy, Emily. She wants to raise at least 25 guide dog puppies!

"Puppy-raising has been such an amazing adventure," she says. "It is so cool being able to do something I love and help someone at the same time!"

AN EYE DOCTOR FOR ANIMALS

Jane Cho spends lots of time learning about the eyes of animals, from hamsters and mice to horses, cows, seals, and sled dogs. The more she learns, the more she can teach others how to care for their pets.

"Ever since I was a young child, I've wanted to help animals because they can't help themselves when they're hurt," Jane says. She has cared for animals' eyes from New York all the way to Alaska!

Eye Care

Eating spinach, carrots, and blueberries is good for your eyes!

Animals need care and so do YOU

Animals need food, water, and exercise to stay healthy.

Match each animal with anything that helps it stay healthy.

Healthy Habits

When the flower friends feel droopy, they take a sip of water.

What do you do when you are thirsty?

_____

What do you do when you are hungry?

_____

My Story
Keeps on Going

**I can care for ANIMALS
and I can care for MYSELF.**

Now, I want to teach others _____

_____

_____

_____

_____

_____